A Ladybird Book

Series 563

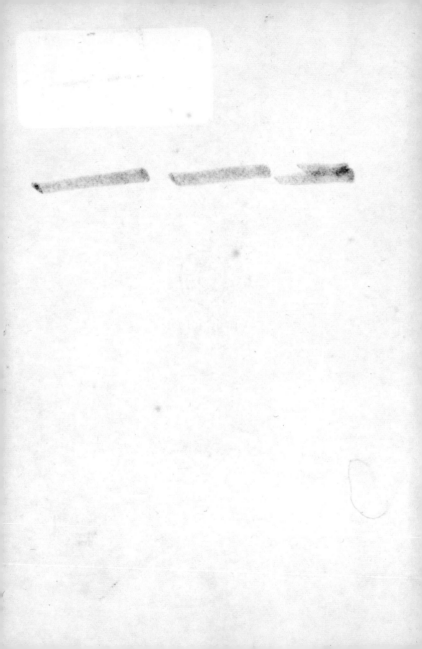

THE ZOO

A LADYBIRD LEARNING TO READ BOOK

by
M. E. GAGG, N.F.U.

with illustrations by
BARRY DRISCOLL

Publishers: Wills & Hepworth Ltd., Loughborough
First published 1960   ©   *Printed in England*

This is the Zoo.

Here are the lions.

Here are
the lion cubs.

Can you see the tiger?

The tiger cubs
are playing

The monkeys
are here.

They like to climb
and jump.

Here are
the elephants.

They like to play
with water.

Look at
the giraffe.

Can you see how tall he is?

Here are
the camels.

There is
a baby camel too.

Can you see the brown bear?

The baby bears
like syrup.

Look at
the Polar bears.

They like to be
in the water.

Here are
the kangaroos.

Can you see
the baby kangaroo?

Look at
the sea lions.

They like fish
for dinner.

The penguins like fish too.

Here is a big, fat
hippopotamus.

I like the panda,
do you?

A Ladybird Book

Series 563